K. JOHNSON.

C000148263

UNDERSTAN[D]
PHONICS
BOOK C

Rita Ray

Contents

Folens Publishers

Phonic elements in Folens *Sounds OK* and *Understanding Phonics*

Phonic element	Sounds OK							Understanding Phonics						
	A	B	C	1	2	3	4	A	B	C	1	2	3	4
consonants b, c, m, t, s, h	●	●	●					●	●	●				
consonants l, d, n, g, f, r, p	●	●	●					●	●	●				
vowels – short a, i	●		●	●				●		●	●			
initial sounds	●		●					●		●				
final sounds	●		●		●			●		●		●		
consonants j, w, x, v, k, y		●		●					●		●			
vowels – short u, o, e		●		●					●		●			
vowel/consonant digraphs		●	●	●	●				●	●	●	●		
double consonants ss, ll, ff		●							●					
consonant blends		●			●	●	●		●			●	●	●
vowel digraphs		●			●	●			●			●	●	
consonant digraphs		●	●			●	●		●	●			●	●
the alphabet				●	●						●	●		
modifying e				●							●			
soft c, g					●	●	●					●	●	●
ph, ch					●							●		
syllables						●	●						●	●
-tion, -sion, -ssion						●	●						●	●
homophones						●	●						●	●
wh, qu							●							●
silent letters						●	●						●	●
suffixes/prefixes						●	●						●	●
-ent, -ant endings						●	●						●	●
-ous, -ary, -ery						●							●	
-act, -uct endings							●							●
-able, -ible endings							●							●

Editor: Michael Spilling
Layout artist: Patricia Hollingsworth
Illustrations: Karen Tushingham of Maggy Mundy Agency Ltd
Cover design: Kim Ashby and Design for Marketing Ltd, Ware

© 1996 Folens Limited, on behalf of the author.
Reprinted 1997.

Every effort has been made to contact copyright holders of material used in this book. If any have been overlooked, we will be pleased to make any necessary arrangements.
First published 1996 by Folens Limited, Dunstable and Dublin.
Folens Limited, Albert House, Apex Business Centre, Boscombe Road, Dunstable, LU5 4RL, United Kingdom.

ISBN 1 85276 899-1   Printed in Singapore by Craft Print.

Introduction

The intention of this resource is to build up phonic skills and knowledge in a structured way. At the same time, the activities are fun and provide motivation.

The set of activities in Folens' *Understanding Phonics Book C* provide practice in consonant blends at the beginnings and endings of words as well as vowel digraphs. Each set of activities includes an element of comprehension. The children can demonstrate understanding, within a context, of the sounds and words they have learned.

Each resource consists of 45 activities. The activities in *Understanding Phonics Book C* are intended for use with 6–7 year olds, but would be appropriate for children of any age who need to learn basic phonic skills. *Understanding Phonics* can be used alongside any reading programme, either in sequence or selectively, as different needs are identified. The activities link reading and writing and help to give children the basic skills and confidence to attempt independent written work. The progression is based on the graded phonic patterns in Folens' photocopiable *Sounds OK C.*

This programme has some special features:

- It is based on a knowledge of the way children learn. The first activities in a letter group provide a great deal of support as the child is required to find or trace the letter or blend of letters. There are activities that require the children to respond to what they have learned by, for example, drawing objects or completing a puzzle. In this way, progression is built-in and learning reinforced.

- The activities focus directly on the sound to be learned. There are no distracting features to lead the child's attention away from the letter itself.

- The activities for each set of letters are sequenced, rather than offering a one-off tracing and matching exercise without structure and reinforcement.

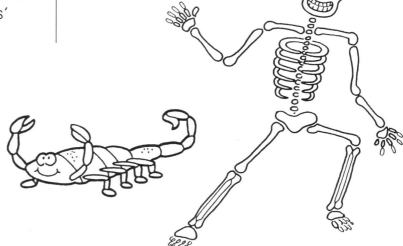

sp sc sk sw

Colour sp ⬭ red. ✏

spider

spade

spoon

spaghetti

Colour the sp words ⬭ red. ✏

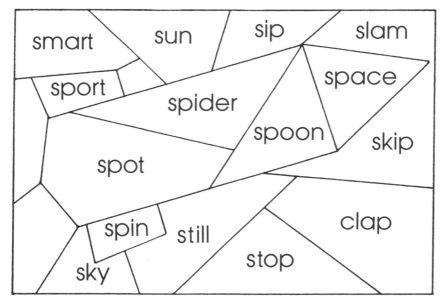

Read and draw:
a big spider.

Can you see a spaceship?

Understanding Phonics – Book C

sp sc sk sw

Colour SC  blue.

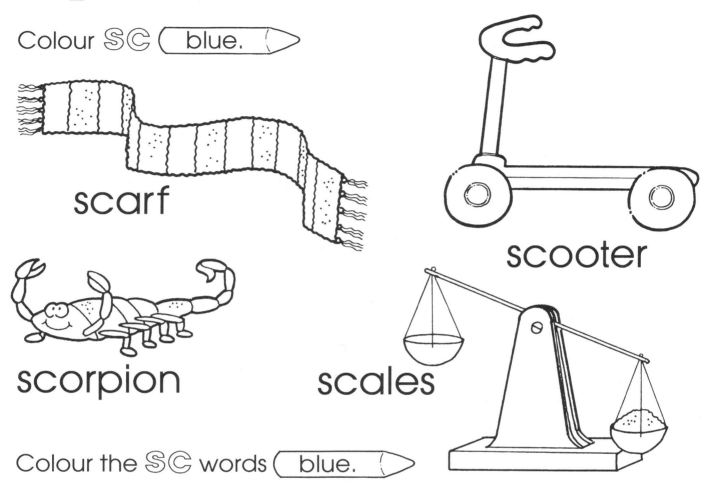

scarf

scooter

scorpion

scales

Colour the SC words  blue.

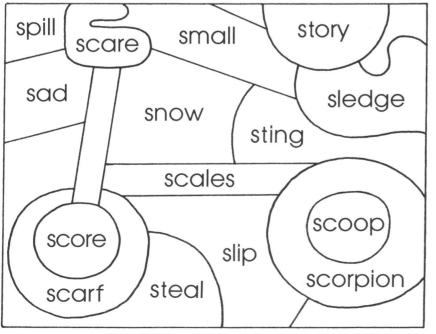

spill
scare
small
story
sad
snow
sting
sledge
scales
score
scarf
steal
slip
scoop
scorpion

Read and draw:
a red scarf.

sp sc sk sw

Colour sk green.

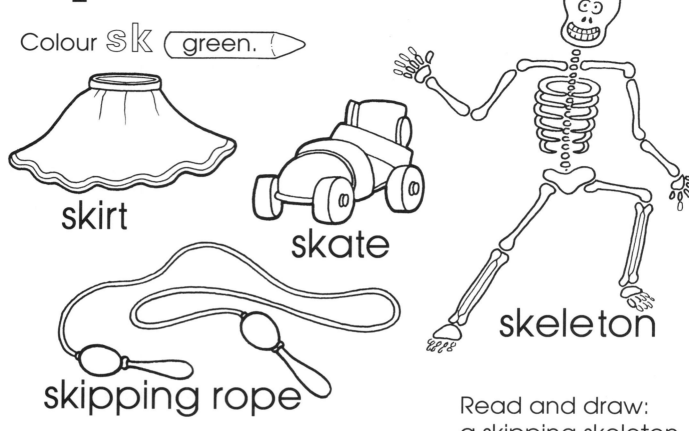

skirt

skate

skeleton

skipping rope

Colour the sk words green.

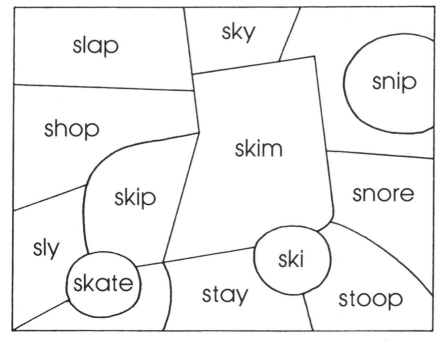

slap   sky   snip

shop   skim

skip   snore

sly

skate   stay   ski   stoop

Read and draw:
a skipping skeleton.

Understanding Phonics – Book C   © Folens (copiable page)

sp sc sk sw

Colour SW yellow.

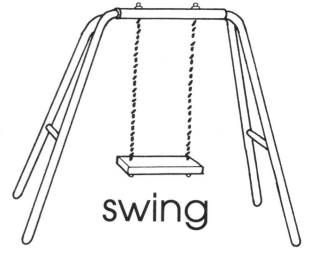

swim

swan

sweets

swing

Colour the SW words yellow.

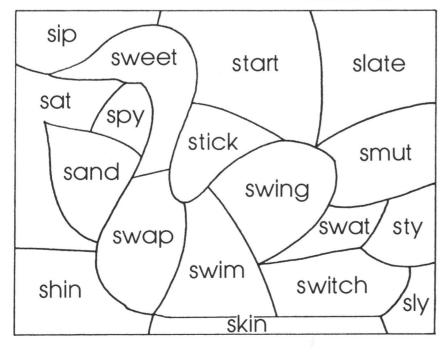

sip
sweet
start
slate
sat
spy
stick
smut
sand
swing
swap
swat
sty
swim
switch
sly
shin
skin

Read and draw:
a yellow sweet.

gl bl fr br

gl → ass   glass   bl → ot   blot

gl → ue   _____   bl → ouse   _____

gl → obe   _____   bl → ossom   _____

gl → ove   _____   bl → anket   _____

✏ Write the words.

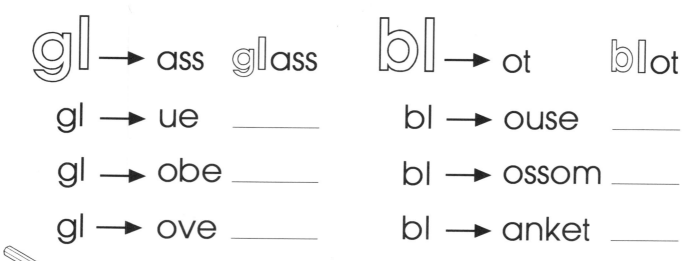

	blot glass ~~blouse~~ globe blossom glue blanket glove	
		blouse

Understanding Phonics – Book C   © Folens (copiable page)

gl bl fr br

fr → og   frog   br → ick   brick

fr → uit   _____   br → ead   _____

fr → idge _____   br → idge   _____

fr → ill   _____   br → ush   _____

Write the words.

	frill	
	frog brick fruit bread fridge bridge ~~frill~~ brush	

gl bl fr br

Find three words with bl.

Find three words with fr.

Colour them (blue.

q	w	s	f	r	o	g	p	l	k
z	b	l	o	u	s	e	y	x	t
m	k	b	l	a	n	k	e	t	w
v	f	r	u	i	t	j	x	q	y
b	l	o	s	s	o	m	p	z	n
r	s	f	r	i	d	g	e	k	g

✏ Draw the pictures.

fridge	blanket	fruit
blouse	frog	blossom

Understanding Phonics – Book C

gl bl fr br

Find three words with br.

Find three words with gl.

Colour them (yellow.

w	g	l	u	e	q	w	r	s	z
f	j	k	m	b	r	u	s	h	y
z	v	g	l	a	s	s	w	k	m
m	j	x	y	g	l	o	v	e	j
k	b	r	i	d	g	e	n	q	v
l	f	h	g	b	r	i	c	k	n

 Draw the pictures.

bridge	glove	brick
glue	brush	glass

Understanding Phonics – Book C

fl pl cl sl

Colour fl (yellow.)

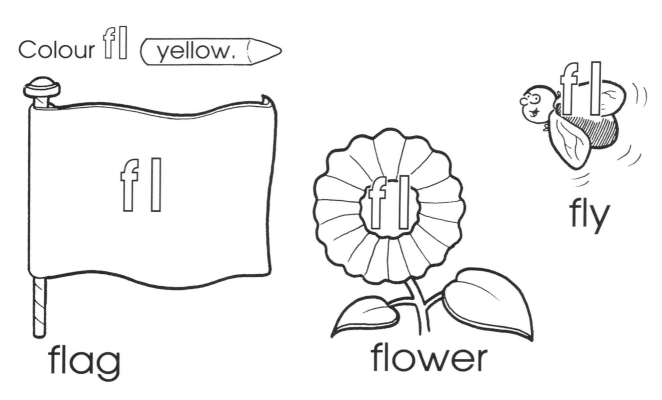

flag

flower

fly

Find the words with fl.
Colour them (yellow.)

	flag	
	stag	
grower	fl	fly
flower		sky
	grip	
	flip	

Read and draw:
a fly on a flower.

Understanding Phonics – Book C

fl pl cl sl

Colour pl green.

plug

Colour pl green.

planet

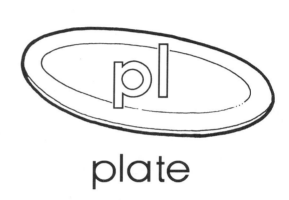
plate

Find the words with pl.
Colour them green.

	plate	
	grate	
thug	pl	planet
plug		crane
	play	
	fray	

Read and draw:
a plug on a plate.

fl pl cl sl

Colour cl blue.

cloud

clown

clock

Find the words with cl.
Colour them blue.

	clown	
	brown	
proud	cl	clock
cloud		frock
	pray	
	clay	

Read and draw:
a clown on a cloud.

Understanding Phonics – Book C

© Folens (copiable page)

fl pl cl sl

Colour sl orange.

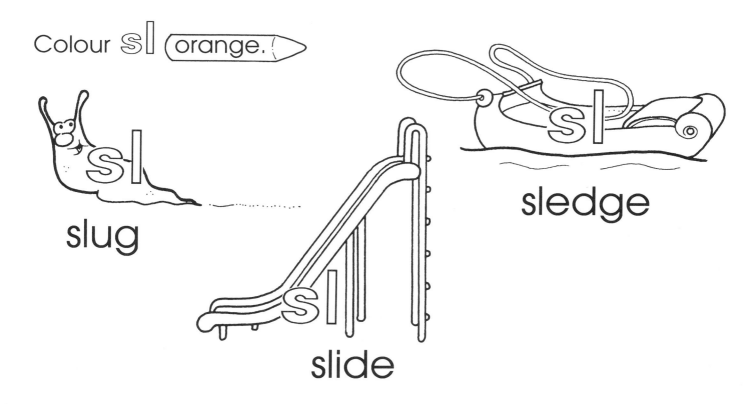

slug

slide

sledge

Find the words with sl.
Colour them orange.

	sledge	
	dredge	
slide	sl	rug
bride		slug
	drip	
	slip	

Read and draw:
a slug on a sledge.

st gr cr dr

st → amp **st**amp   gr → ass   **gr**ass

st → ool _____   gr → apes _____

st → ick _____   gr → avy   _____

st → ar   _____   gr → id   _____

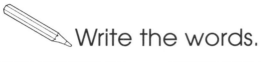 Write the words.

	stool grapes grid stamp stick grass ~~gravy~~ star	gravy

st gr cr dr

cr→own   crown   dr→um   drum

cr → ab   _____   dr → ess   _____

cr → isps   _____   dr → agon   _____

cr → acker   _____   dr → iver   _____

✎ Write the words.

	driver crab crisps dress dragon crown cracker drum	
driver		

st gr cr dr

Colour three words with st  (yellow.)

Colour three words with gr (blue.)

m	w	s	t	a	r	v	w	y	z
y	z	v	q	b	g	r	a	s	s
b	s	t	o	o	l	d	j	k	m
k	g	g	r	a	p	e	s	q	r
s	m	j	l	s	t	a	m	p	k
w	g	r	i	d	j	z	q	r	x

Draw the pictures.

grid	stamp	grapes
star	grass	stool

Understanding Phonics – Book C   © Folens (copiable page)

st gr cr dr

Colour three words with **cr** [yellow.]

Colour three words with **dr** [blue.]

b	a	j	c	r	o	w	n	y	z
k	d	r	a	g	o	n	q	v	w
f	j	k	m	c	r	a	b	z	y
l	n	p	r	t	v	d	r	u	m
w	c	r	a	c	k	e	r	b	k
l	n	s	d	r	e	s	s	r	d

Draw the pictures.

dress	cracker	drum
crown	dragon	crab

Understanding Phonics – Book C

pr tr

Colour pr red.

pram

present

princess

Write the pr words in the pram.

prince   clown   print   drop   shark
ground   pray   pram   prize   press

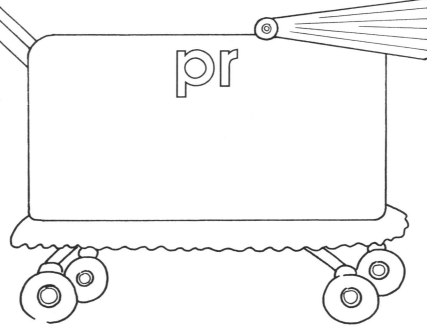

Understanding Phonics – Book C

pr tr

Colour tr  blue.

treasure

tree

trumpet

Write the tr words in the tree.

train   grim   tram   triangle   free
brain   trap   cart   drag   tree

pr tr

Colour the **pr** words (red.)

Colour the **tr** words (blue.)

tray

tram

trim

trolley

trick

trap

tree

blot

stick

snow

shop

brown

blow

print

prince

prize

pray

pram

Understanding Phonics – Book C

© Folens (copiable page)

pr tr

Colour six words with pr (yellow.)

Colour six words with tr (blue.)

q	w	t	r	o	l	l	e	y	z	w
b	p	r	e	s	e	n	t	l	k	v
t	r	a	p	z	p	r	i	z	e	n
m	t	r	i	a	n	g	l	e	k	m
p	r	i	n	t	e	r	z	p	r	y
t	r	a	i	n	w	p	r	o	o	f
p	r	i	n	c	e	v	t	r	a	m
m	t	r	u	m	p	e	t	k	z	v

 Write the words in the boxes.

present   triangle   tram
trap   pry   prince
prize   trolley   proof
train   printer   trumpet

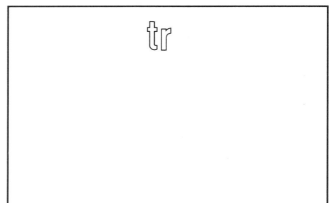

pr

tr

Happy families game

2–4 players can play.
Make the cube on page 26.
Cut out the cards.

How to play

1. Put the cards face up in six sets.
2. Roll the cube.
3. Pick a card to match the letters.
4. Collect as many 'families' as you can.
   For example: a family would be **cl**.
   A family has four cards.

| clap | club | clock | claw |
| flower | flag | flat | fly |

Understanding Phonics – Book C

Happy families game

plum	plug	plant	play
drum	drink	drill	dress
stop	stick	star	stag
crab	cry	crop	cress

Happy families game

Cut these lines: _____

Fold these lines: _ _ _ _ _ _

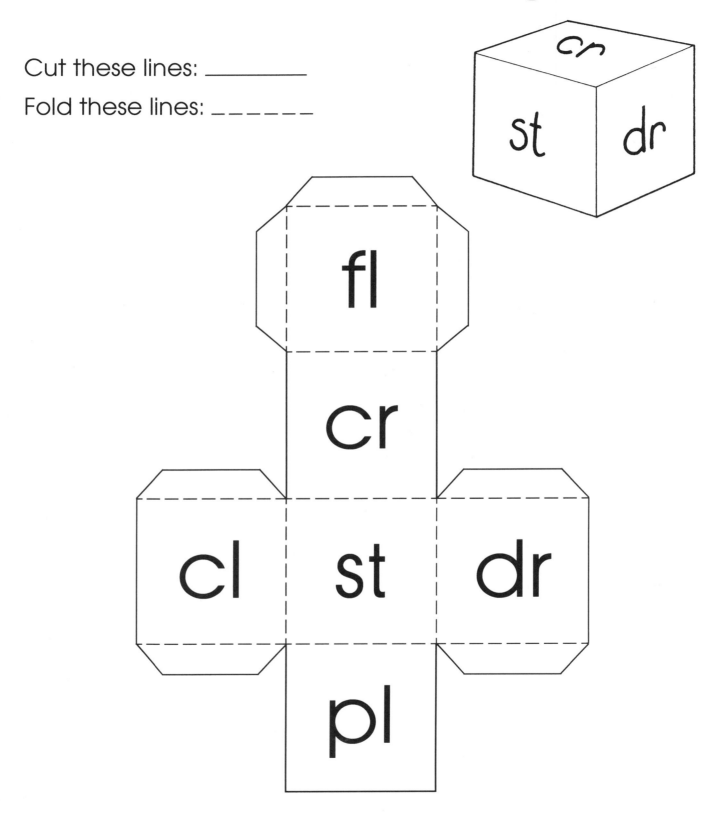

Understanding Phonics – Book C   © Folens (copiable page)

Happy families

Make the wheel.

Turn the pointer.

Read the words.

Write sentences about six of the words.

1. _____

2. _____

3. _____

4. _____

5. _____

6. _____

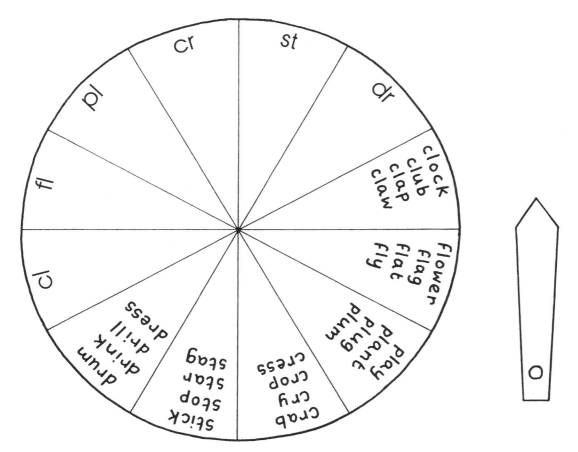

mp lp sk lk lt nd sp nt st

Katy wants to go to the camp.
Colour the mp words (yellow.)
Follow the path.

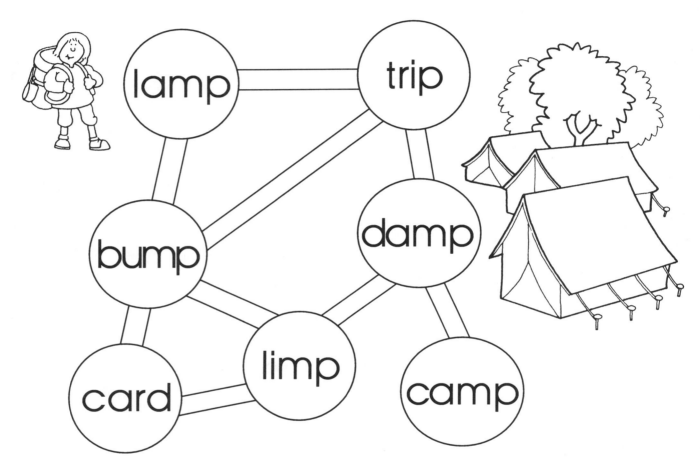

Colour the lp words (green.)

help	bark	plan	yelp
drum	gulp	flap	pram
grate	push	pulp	glad

Understanding Phonics – Book C

mp lp sk lk lt nd sp nt st

Colour sk ⟨ red. ⟩
Say the words.

mask   desk

ask   risk   dusk   cask

Colour lk ⟨ blue. ⟩
Say the words.

walk   talk   stalk

Read the sentences.

1. Walk to the class.
2. Ask for some crisps.
3. Put on the mask.
4. Talk to a friend.

mp lp sk lk lt nd sp nt st

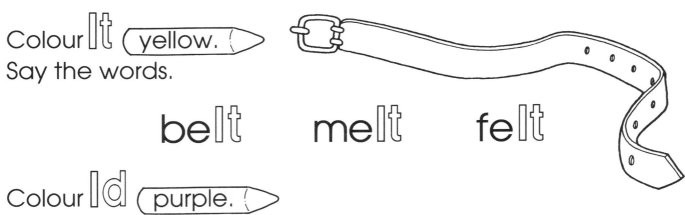

Colour **lt** (yellow.)
Say the words.

be**lt**   me**lt**   fe**lt**

Colour **ld** (purple.)
Say the words.

go**ld**   co**ld**   so**ld**

Look at the words on the quilt.

Colour the **lt** words (yellow.)
Colour the **ld** words (purple.)

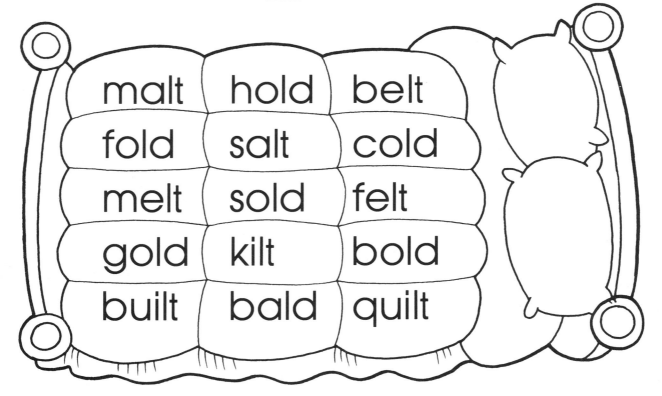

malt	hold	belt
fold	salt	cold
melt	sold	felt
gold	kilt	bold
built	bald	quilt

Understanding Phonics – Book C

mp lp sk lk lt nd sp nt st

Colour nd (orange.)
Say the words.

and   sand   land

Colour sp (green.)
Say the words.

rasp   lisp   clasp

Colour nt (brown.)
Say the words.

ant   lent   sent

Colour st (pink.)
Say the words.

fast   just   best

Write the words in the correct boxes.

-nd	-sp	-nt	-st

sh ch th wh tch

Read the words.

ship

shark

shop

 Write **sh** in the spaces. Read the words.

__ __ark   __ __ip   fi__ __

__ __op   __ __ed   di__ __

Tick (✓) the correct word.

ship
chip

fish
wish

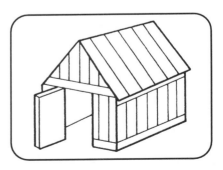

shed
then

Understanding Phonics – Book C

sh ch th wh tch

Read the words.

chips

cherry

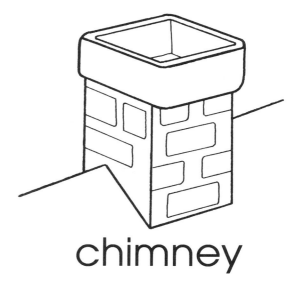

chimney

 Write ch in the spaces. Read the words.

_ _ips   _ _in   _ _erry

_ _imp   _ _ick   in_ _

Tick (✓) the correct word.

chick
thick

chips
chimp

cherry
chimney

sh ch th wh tch

Read the words.

thumb   three   bath

Write **th** in the spaces. Read the words.

_ _ e   _ _ is

_ _ at   _ _ ere

whistle   whiskers

Write **wh** in the spaces. Read the words.

_ _ at   _ _ isper

_ _ ere   _ _ en

Read the sentences.

Where is the cat?
She is there. I can see her whiskers.

Understanding Phonics – Book C

tch

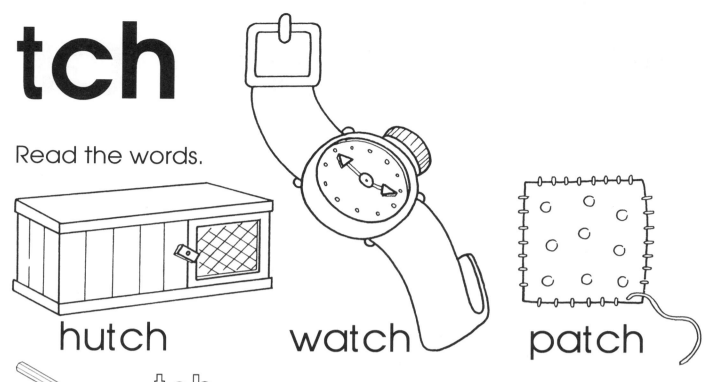

Read the words.

hutch   watch   patch

Write tch in the spaces. Read the words.

ca____   pa____   la____

ki____en   hu____   pi____

Colour the tch words ⟨ blue. ⟩

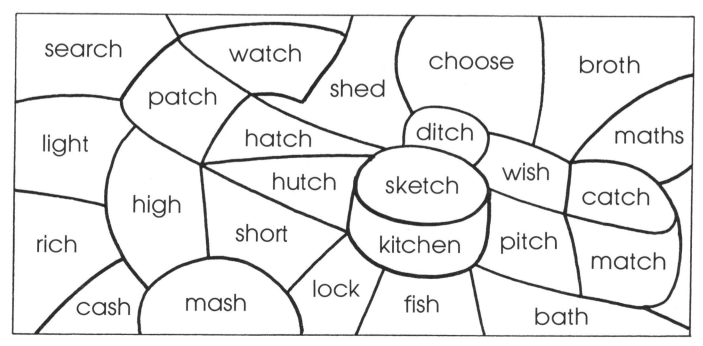

search   watch   choose   broth

patch   shed

light   hatch   ditch   maths

hutch   sketch   wish   catch

high

rich   short   kitchen   pitch   match

cash   mash   lock   fish   bath

What time does the watch show?

wa wo ing ar

Colour wa (red.)

wand

wasp

wall

Colour wo (blue.)

worm

work

words

Write your name: _____

Write your name in the spaces.
Draw pictures.

1. _____ sits on a wall.

2. There is a wasp on

_____ .

3. _____ can see a

worm.

wa wo ing ar

Colour ing (green.

swing

k**ing**

Read and draw.

The wasp stings the king.

✏️ Write your name: _____

Write your name in the spaces.
Draw pictures.

1. _____ on a swing.

2. _____ can sing.

Understanding Phonics – Book C

wa wo ing ar

Add **ing** to the words.

pull_____   talk_____

walk_____   sing_____

Add **ing** to the words. You need to add a letter.

runn_____   hitt_____

digg_____   sitt_____

Add **ing** to the words on the pots.

pick_____
sell_____
play_____

patt_____
robb_____
hopp_____

swing_____
sing_____
sting_____

    Understanding Phonics – Book C

wa wo ing ar

Write ar in the spaces.

c _ _   p _ _ k

b _ _ k   m _ _ k

Put the words in the correct spaces.

bark   **car**

The _____ can go fast.

The dog can _____ .

Colour the ar words red.

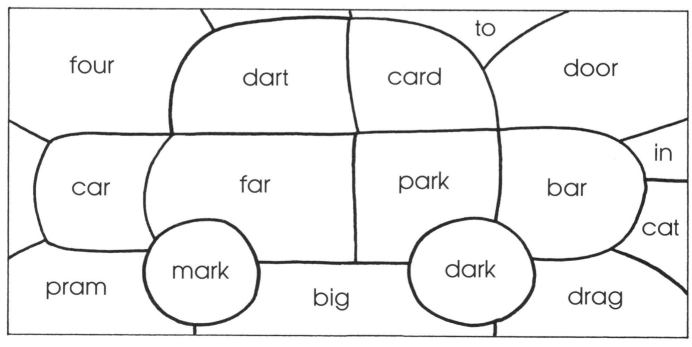

or ng oo ue

Write **or** in the spaces. Read the words.

f_ _ k   c_ _ k   b_ _ n

c_ _ n   t_ _ n   h_ _ se

Draw the missing part of the picture.

A knife and fork.

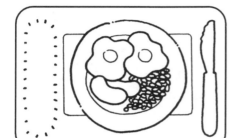

A popping cork.

Help the horse to get to the corn.
Colour the **or** words (green.) Follow the path.

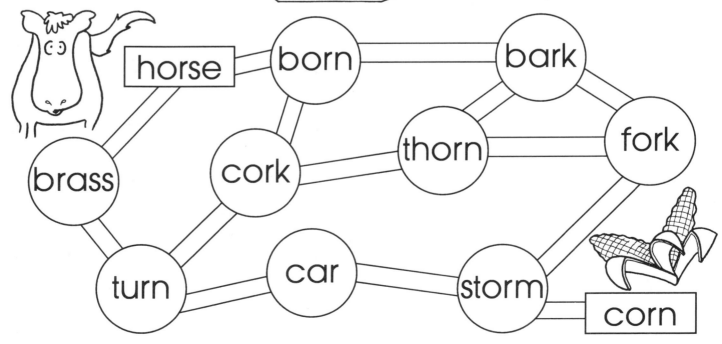

horse   born   bark

brass   cork   thorn   fork

turn   car   storm   corn

Understanding Phonics – Book C   © Folens (copiable page)

or ng oo ue

Read the sentence.
Kim sing**s a lo**ng **so**ng**.

Read and draw:

The bee stung the
dog.

✏️ Write your name: _____
Write your name in the spaces.
Draw pictures.

1. Can _____ sing
   a song?

2. Has _____ been
   stung by a wasp?

3. Here is _____ in
   a long scarf.

or ng oo ue

Read the words.
Write them in the correct shape.

boot	glue	rescue	true
spoon	queue	food	roof
balloon	moon	clue	blue

boot

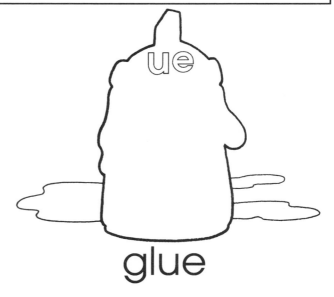

glue

Draw a roof on
the house.

Draw a moon near
the house.

Draw a pool near
the house.

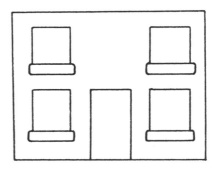

Understanding Phonics – Book C

© Folens (copiable page)

or ng oo ue

Read and draw.

A blue torch.

A pot of glue.

A red balloon.

A long queue.

Sam's cat is up a tree.
How can she rescue it?

Draw a picture of the
rescue.

The rescue

ew

Read the ew words.

new   flew   blew

Read the story.

 Write what happened next.
Draw a picture.

Ram had a blue balloon. The wind blew. Ram's balloon flew up. It flew to the school and fell down on to the roof.

What happened next?

_____

_____

_____

_____

_____

_____

_____

Understanding Phonics – Book C

ai ay

Read the ay words.

play   day   way

Draw what you do on:

Saturday	Monday	Friday

ai words.

Write your name: _____

Write your name in the spaces.
Draw pictures.

1. _____ on a train.

2. _____ paints a
picture.

3. _____ bangs a
nail in the wall.

ee ea

Read the ee words.

tree   sheep   sweet   three

Read the ea words.

tea   read   leaf   bean

Choose the word.

   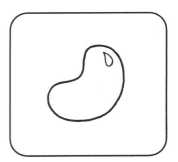

leaf   tea   sweet   bean

three   tree   bean   sheep

Look at the 10 pictures.
Find their names in the puzzle.

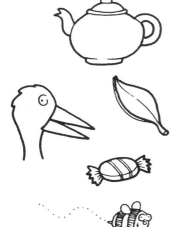

s	h	e	e	p	x	b	e	a	n
k	l	e	a	f	z	t	r	e	e
s	w	e	e	t	w	v	b	e	e
p	t	h	r	e	e	q	s	e	a
b	e	a	k	n	m	j	k	l	m
y	z	x	t	e	a	p	o	t	w

    Understanding Phonics – Book C

ow oa

Read the ow words.

Read and draw:

Blow, blow, blow,
Make the windmill go.

Snowdrops can grow
in the winter snow.

Read the oa words.

boat   goat   coat

Draw a boat floating
on the sea.

Draw a goat in the
boat.

Draw a coat on the
goat.

Understanding Phonics – Book C

Snail trail

You need to make a spinner.
Two can play.

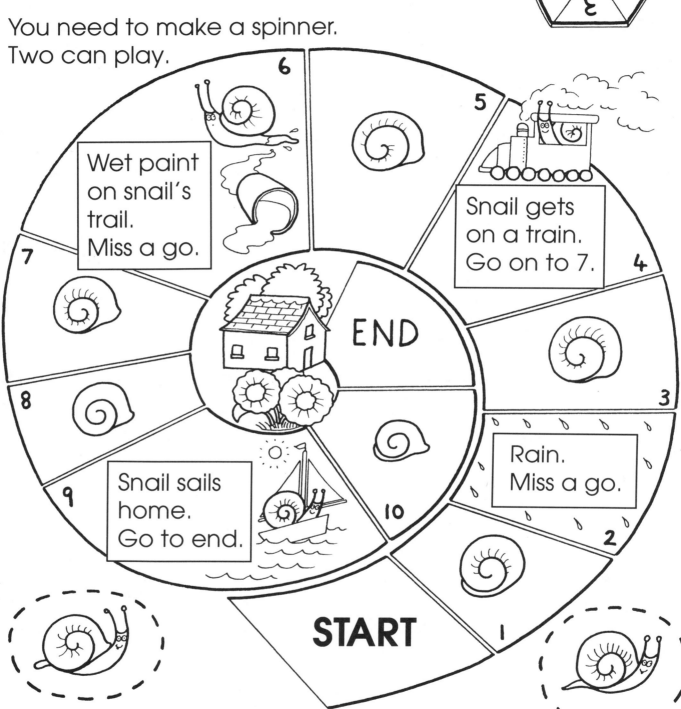

✂ Cut out the snails. Each player should colour
them differently. Take turns to spin the spinner.
Move your snail that number of places.

Understanding Phonics – Book C